Developing Num

USING AND APPLYING MATHS

INVESTIGATIONS FOR THE DAILY MATHS LESSON

F. Hooper

year

2

Hilary Koll and Steve Mills

A & C BLACK

Mathematical skills and processes

Page	Activity title	Predict	Visualise	Look for pattern	Record	Reason	Make decisions	Estimate	Explain	Be systematic	Co-operate	Compare	Test ideas	Trial and improvement	Ask own questions	Generalise	Check
	Numbers and the number system																
13	Number maker			●		○	○			●					○		○
14	Hearty puzzles			○		●				○		○			○	●	○
15	Seating plan	○		●		●				○		○	○			○	
16	Halfway house		○	●		○				○			○			●	
17	Fair shares					○				○	○		○			●	
18	An odd puzzle		○		○	○	○			○			●	●			
19	Months of the year			●		○				○			○			○	
20	Don't bug me!	○	○						●		●	○	○				
21	Changing groups			●		○				○	●	○	○				○
	Calculations																
22	Nine planets			●		○				○		●	○		○		○
23	Supermarket challenge		○			●			○	○		●	○	●			○
24	Mystery money			○	○	○				○		●	○				
25	Switch the units			○		●				○		○	○			●	
26	Trailer tricks	○		●		○				●			○		○		
27	Dial a word				○	○	●						○		●		
28	Playing pool					○	○	○				○		●			
29	Digit sums			●		○				●	○	○					○
30–31	Pick 'n' mix: 1 and 2			○	○		●			○	○	○		●			
32	Guess if it's less	●							●			○	○				
33	Spot the difference	●		●		○				○		○	○			○	
	Measures, shape and space																
34	Letter trails: 1			○						●							●
35	Letter trails: 2	●		○						○				●			○
36	X marks the square				●	○			○	○		○	●	●			○
37	Chuckle the clown		○	○						●							
38	Secret shapes		●			○						○					
39–40	Timetables and rotas: 1 and 2					●	●		○						○		
41	Wriggling worms	●	○						●				○				
42	Mystery tour		●		○		●	○			○		○				
43	Spinning around	○	○	●		●				○			○			○	
44	Balancing act		○							○	○	○	●	●			
45	Spot the shape		○	○		○	○		●			●	○				
46–47	Jigsaw: 1 and 2		○			●				○					●	○	
48	Shape sequences		●	○		●	○			○		○	○				

● Key processes identified on the activity sheet   ○ Additional processes involved in the activity

Contents

Reprinted 2006

Published 2005 by A & C Black Publishers Limited
38 Soho Square, London W1D 3HB
www.acblack.com

ISBN-10: 0-7136-7137-8
ISBN-13: 978-0-7136-7137-7

Copyright text © Hilary Koll and Steve Mills, 2005
Copyright illustrations © Pat Murray, 2005
Copyright cover illustration © Charlotte Hard, 2005
Editors: Lynne Williamson and Marie Lister
Designer: Heather Billin

The authors and publishers would like to thank Jane McNeill and Catherine Yemm for their advice in producing this series of books.

A CIP catalogue record for this book is available from the British Library.

Printed and Bound in Great Britain by Cromwell Press Ltd, Trowbridge, Wiltshire.

This book is produced using paper that is made from wood grown in managed, sustainable forests. It is natural, renewable and recyclable. The logging and manufacturing processes conform to the environmental regulations of the country of origin.

Introduction

Developing Numeracy: Using and Applying Maths is a series of seven photocopiable activity books designed to be used during the daily maths lesson. The books focus on using and applying mathematics, as referred to in the National Numeracy Strategy *Framework for teaching mathematics*. The activities are intended to be used in the time allocated to pupil activities during the main part of the lesson. They are designed to develop and reinforce the skills and processes that are vital to help children use and apply their maths.

Using and applying mathematics

There are several different components which make up the **content** of maths and form the bulk of any maths curriculum:

- **mathematical facts**, for example, a triangle has three sides;
- **mathematical skills**, such as counting;
- **mathematical concepts**, like place value.

For maths teaching to be successful, it is vital that children can *use* this mathematical content beyond their classroom, either in real-life situations or as a basis for further understanding. However, in order to do so, they require extra abilities over and above the mathematical content they have learned. These extra abilities are often referred to as the **processes** of mathematical activity. It is these processes which make mathematical content usable.

As an example, consider this question:
How many triangles are there in this shape?

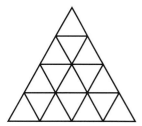

The mathematical content required is only:
- the **fact** that a triangle has three sides;
- the **skill** of counting.

As such, it could be expected that very young children could solve this problem. The fact that they cannot suggests that other abilities are involved. These are the processes, and for this question they include:
- visualising the different-sized triangles;
- being systematic in counting all the triangles of different sizes;
- looking for patterns in the numbers of triangles;
- trial and improvement;
- recording.

Unless children can apply these processes in this situation, then however good their counting skills and knowledge of triangles may be, they will fail.

The 'solving problems' strand of the *Framework for teaching mathematics* emphasises the importance of using and applying mathematics. This series of books is intended to make explicit the skills and processes involved in learning how to put maths knowledge to use.

Using and Applying Maths Year 2 supports the development of the using and applying processes by providing opportunities to introduce and practise them through a series of activities. On the whole these activities are designed for children to work on independently, although this is not always possible and occasionally some children may need support.

Pre-school children are naturally inquisitive about the world around them. They love to explore and experiment, and to make marks and record things on paper in their own idiosyncratic ways. Unfortunately, once at school the focus is often placed firmly on the maths content alone and children can be led to believe that maths is not a subject of exploration, but rather one of simply learning the 'right way to do things'. As a result, when older children are asked to explore and investigate maths they are often at a loss if their maths teaching to date has not encouraged and built upon their natural instincts.

Year 2 helps children to develop the following processes:
- predicting
- visualising
- looking for pattern
- recording
- reasoning
- making decisions
- estimating
- explaining
- being systematic
- co-operating
- comparing
- testing ideas
- trial and improvement
- asking own questions
- generalising
- checking

When using these activities, the focus need not be on the actual mathematical content. Instead, the teacher's demonstrations, discussions and questioning should emphasise the processes the children are using. A summary of the skills and processes covered by each activity is shown on page 2. When appropriate, invite the children to explain their thinking to others. Research has shown that children develop processes most successfully when the teacher encourages them to act as experts rather than novices, allowing them to work autonomously and encouraging a range of approaches to any problem rather than constraining discussion to produce an overall class plan. The children should evaluate their own plans against other plans in the posing, planning and monitoring phases of the lessons.

Extension

Many of the activity sheets end with a challenge (**Now try this!**) which reinforces and extends children's learning, and provides the teacher with an opportunity for assessment. On occasion, it may be helpful to read the instructions with the children before they begin the activity. For some of the challenges the children will need to record their answers on a separate piece of paper.

Organisation

Very little equipment is needed, but it will be useful to have the following resources available: coloured pencils, counters, scissors, glue, coins, squared paper, number lines and number tracks.

To help teachers select appropriate learning experiences for the children, the activities are grouped into sections within the book. However, the activities are not expected to be used in this order unless stated otherwise. The sheets are intended to support, rather than direct, the teacher's planning.

Some activities can be made easier or more challenging by masking or substituting numbers. You may wish to re-use pages by copying them onto card and laminating them.

Teachers' notes

Brief notes are provided at the foot of each page giving ideas and suggestions for maximising the effectiveness of the activity sheets. These can be masked before copying.

Solutions and further explanations of the activities can be found on pages 7–12, together with examples of questions that you can ask.

Whole class warm-up activities

The following activities provide some practical ideas which can be used to introduce the main teaching part of the lesson.

Number scarves

This activity focuses on predicting a sequence of numbers in tens or ones, starting from any two-digit number. Draw a scarf on the board and fill in several numbers, counting on in either ones or tens, for example:

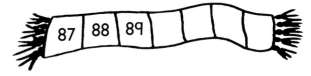

Ask the children to predict how the sequence will continue. Similarly, you can start from any two-digit number and count back, for example:

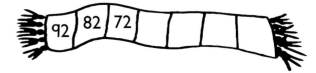

Again, ask the children to predict how the sequence will continue.

Estimate it

Hold up several fingers or pens and then quickly hide them behind your back. Ask: *How many fingers/pens did you see?* Write several of the children's estimates on the board. Show them the true answer and discuss the estimates.

Visualise it

Describe shapes inside the classroom, or that can be seen through the windows: for example, *I can see a sphere in the classroom. What am I looking at? I can see a cuboid through the window. What am I looking at?* Children should raise their hands when they think they know the answer.

People sort

Count the number of children in the class. Select individuals to sort the children into groups: for example, 'trousers/skirts', 'hair ribbon/no hair ribbon'. Less clear-cut distinctions, such as 'fair hair/dark hair', 'long hair/short hair', 'tall/not tall', can be used to stimulate discussion. Once the children have been sorted into groups, ask questions about the groups: for example, *Who thinks Jess has short hair? Who would put Emma in the 'tall' group?*

Notes on the activities

Numbers and the number system

Number maker (page 13)

☆ *Processes: be systematic, look for pattern, reason, make decisions, ask own questions, check*

If the children choose to include the original six numbers in their list, there are 15 possibilities; if not, there are 9:

79	77	72
29	27	22
89	87	82
(9	7	2
70	20	80)

Answers are as follows:

1. 15 (or 9 if the original numbers are not included)
2. **(a)** 7 (or 5)
   (b) 4 (or 3)
   (c) 2
   (d) 7 (or 3)
   (e) 8 (or 6)
   (f) 8 (or 6)

Suggested questions:
- Do you think you have found all the numbers?
- How could you order your numbers to check?
- What other questions could you ask about your answers? Which is your largest/smallest number?

Hearty puzzles (page 14)

☆ *Processes: reason, generalise, be systematic, compare, trial and improvement, check, look for pattern*

The following 11 numbers can be 'heart numbers':

34	36	38		
42	43	44	46	48
62	63	64		

Answers are:

(a) 11   **(b)** 0   **(c)** 4

Discuss why a number beginning with 8 can never be a heart number. Children who try the extension activity should discover that 18 different heart numbers are possible when the six digits are all different. None of the numbers will begin with the lowest or highest digit in the set. Three heart numbers will contain the lowest digit and three will contain the highest digit.

Suggested questions:
- What have you found out?
- How many heart numbers have you found?
- Which numbers cannot be heart numbers? Why not?

Seating plan (page 15)

☆ *Processes: look for pattern, reason, predict, generalise, explain, test ideas, compare*

In this activity the children look for patterns in the arrangements of multiples of 3 in number grids. It will be helpful to revise the 3 times table at the start of the lesson. The children should notice and begin to generalise about the patterns in the following way.

If the number of seats per row is:
- a multiple of 3, straight line patterns of circles are produced;
- one fewer than a multiple of 3, diagonal lines of circles sloping up to the right are produced;
- one greater than a multiple of 3, diagonal lines of circles sloping up to the left are produced.

The children could go on to explore other patterns: for example, circling multiples of 4 or 5. They could test the question: 'When we circle multiples of 4, how many seats per row do we need to make a straight line?'

Suggested questions:
- What patterns do the multiples of 3 form?
- Can you explain your thinking to us?
- What did you predict? Were you right?

Halfway house (page 16)

☆ *Processes: look for pattern, generalise, visualise, explain, reason, test ideas*

This activity shows the children that the number halfway between two multiples of 10 can be found by adding the multiples of 10 and halving the answer. The children are encouraged to choose their own numbers and to devise their own strategies for finding the halfway number. These might involve writing all the numbers between the two circle numbers; counting on and back; knowing that 5 is half of 10 and adding 5 to the lower number; using known number facts, and so on. Once the children have discovered the strategy of adding the circle numbers and halving the answer, they should be encouraged to try other numbers to check that this approach always works.

Suggested questions/prompts:
- Which numbers have you chosen?
- Explain to us how you worked out the halfway number.
- Did anyone else do it a different way?
- What did you notice?
- Do you think this always works?

Fair shares (page 17)

☆ *Processes: generalise, reason, explain, co-operate, test ideas*

This activity can help the children to formalise their thinking about odd and even numbers. Through working practically with counters, they will see the effects of sharing odd and even numbers of objects between two people. The children should notice that:
- an even number divides exactly by two;
- there is 1 left over when an odd number is divided by 2.

Suggested questions:
- What do you notice?
- Do you think this is always true?
- What do you think would happen if you were to share sweets between three people?

An odd puzzle (page 18)

☆ *Processes: test ideas, trial and improvement, make
decisions, reason, record, be systematic, visualise*

This puzzle has a number of different routes that involve
fewer than five odd numbers. Some of these routes begin
with two odd numbers, and the children may be put off
them by having to give up two cubes immediately – but
they will find the routes better in the long run. Ask the
children to think about what they have learned from each
route they try, to move them on from trial and improvement
approaches. Recording E or O (even or odd) next to the
numbers will be helpful. As an extension activity, the
children could make their own puzzle of this type. Cubes
could be given up every time a multiple of 5 or 10 is
reached.

Suggested questions/prompts:

● Which ways have you tried? Make a record of your
routes. What have you learned from these routes?

● What strategies could you use? Could you try working
backwards from the finish?

Months of the year (page 19)

☆ *Processes: look for pattern, reason, explain,
compare, generalise*

The children should notice that all pairs of numbers for the
months of the year total 11. Encourage them to explain
why this number is produced. Similarly, for the extension
activity, the children should begin to generalise what they
think the two numbers will add up to (29). You could ask
them to investigate the totals for other months.

Suggested questions:

● What do you notice?

● Did you find a quick way of answering the questions?

Don't bug me! (page 20)

☆ *Processes: estimate, co-operate, predict, visualise,
test ideas, compare*

When estimating, ensure the children appreciate that they
should not actually count the objects but just get a sense
of how many there might be. Encourage discussion about
what is a good estimate.

Suggested questions:

● How many bugs do you think there are on this leaf?

● What makes you think that?

● Did you get better at guessing towards the end? What
helped you?

Changing groups (page 21)

☆ *Processes: be systematic, look for pattern, reason,
explain, compare, co-operate, check*

Some children may benefit from being given six counters
to work with. Young children sometimes lose heart if they
feel they cannot find all the ways. When they begin to
show signs of frustration, ask them to join forces with a
partner and compare their findings to see whether they
can help each other.

The ten ways should be ordered as follows:

Two groups		Three groups	
1 5		1 1 4	
2 4		1 2 3	
3 3	3 ways	2 2 2	3 ways
Four groups		**Five groups**	
1 1 1 3		1 1 1 1 2	1 way
1 1 2 2	2 ways	**Six groups**	
		1 1 1 1 1 1	1 way

Encourage the children to explain why there can only be
one way of making six groups when there are six children.

Now try this! With seven children, the 14 ways are:

1 6, 2 5, 3 4, 1 1 5, 1 2 4, 1 3 3, 2 2 3, 1 1 1 4,
1 1 2 3, 2 2 2 1, 1 1 1 1 3, 1 1 1 2 2, 1 1 1 1 1 2,
1 1 1 1 1 1 1

Suggested questions:

● Have you checked that all your ways are different?

● How can you be sure that you have found all the ways?

● If six children were getting into groups for a
competition, which three ways do you think are the
fairest? (3 3, 2 2 2, or 1 1 1 1 1 1)

● How many ways do you think there are of putting seven
children into seven groups? Can you explain why?

Calculations

Nine planets (page 22)

☆ *Processes: look for pattern, compare, check, explain,
reason, ask own questions*

Encourage the children to discuss the patterns created
with a partner and to suggest reasons for the patterns.

Difference	Number of lines
3	6
4	5
5	4
6	3
7	2
8	1

For the extension activity, the children can be encouraged
to ask their own questions and to choose which other
totals or differences to explore. They could even extend
the investigation by exploring other numbers of planets or
placing them in different arrangements.

Suggested questions:

● Can you describe the pattern you have made?

● How is it different from this pattern?

● Can you see a pattern in the numbers of lines for
each difference?

Supermarket challenge (page 23)

☆ *Processes: trial and improvement, reason, test ideas,
check, visualise, be systematic, explain*

Ask the children to describe any strategies they used when
they were tackling this activity: for example, 'I noticed that
the things in the second aisle were too expensive, so I
didn't bother going down that one again.' 'I noticed that you
had to pick up the first three items every time, so I worked

out the total of those and started from there.' Encourage the children to ask their own questions and to find particular routes: for example, the route with the smallest/largest total or the fewest/most items, or the total closest to £20/£40. As a further extension, the children could devise their own 'supermarket challenge'.

The solution to the puzzle involves going up the first aisle, halfway down the third, halfway back up the fourth and all the way down the fifth to the checkout.

Suggested questions:
● What strategies did you use?
● How could you check your answer?
● What questions could you ask?

Mystery money (page 24)
☆ *Processes: be systematic, compare, check, look for pattern, record, explain, reason*

Discuss with the class ways of working systematically: for example, starting with three 1p coins and changing one coin at a time. Then move on to finding ways with 2p coins, being careful to check that each solution has not already been found. The following totals are possible:

1p + 1p + 1p = 3p
1p + 1p + 2p = 4p
1p + 2p + 2p = 5p
2p + 2p + 2p = 6p
1p + 1p + 5p = 7p
1p + 2p + 5p = 8p
2p + 2p + 5p = 9p
1p + 5p + 5p = 11p
5p + 5p + 2p = 12p
5p + 5p + 5p = 15p

For the extension activity, all the totals between 4p and 27p are possible, as well as 30p, 31p, 32p, 35p and 40p. Some totals can be made in more than one way: for example, 1p + 1p + 10p + 10p or 2p + 5p + 5p + 10p = 22p.

Suggested questions/prompts:
● Which totals can you make? Which cannot be made?
● Talk to your partner about what you did to make sure you had found all the totals.
● What if there were four children with a coin each?

Switch the units (page 25)
☆ *Processes: reason, generalise, explain, look for pattern, compare, test ideas*

Encourage the children to suggest why the totals are the same when the units digits are swapped. They could be given place value cards to help them explain this: for example, 34 + 12 will have the same total as 32 + 14 because both can be partitioned into 30 + 10 + 4 + 2, which totals 46.

Suggested questions:
● What do you notice?
● Can you find other pairs with the same total?
● Do you think this works with any pair of numbers?
● What if we had three-digit numbers?
● What if we swapped the tens digits?

Trailer tricks (page 26)
☆ *Processes: look for pattern, be systematic, predict, test ideas, reason, ask own questions*

Ask the children to explain to others what patterns they notice in the numbers that are produced. Whichever trailer numbers are used, the finish numbers are as follows:

Garage 1: always even
Garage 2: always odd
Garage 3: always end in zero
Garage 4: always end in one

Suggested questions:
● What do all these numbers have in common?
● Do you think this will always be true? Why?
● How could you check?

Dial a word (page 27)
☆ *Processes: ask own questions, make decisions, reason, record, test ideas*

For the extension activity suggested in the Teachers' note at the foot of the sheet, the children should be asked to design a poster showing the questions they asked and the answers that they found. The poster could include a challenge to other children to find further solutions, such as 'Can you find an animal with a larger total?' A display of these posters can create a great deal of interest and can be the focus of useful 'time-fillers'.

Suggested questions/prompts:
● What topic have you chosen?
● What questions could you ask?
● Explain to us what your poster shows.

Playing pool (page 28)
☆ *Processes: trial and improvement, reason, record, be systematic, compare, make decisions*

Encourage the children to discuss strategies, such as working out that 10 must be the top number since the balls total 55 and the other rows total 45. Solutions include the following (the numbers in each row can be written in any order):

Top row	10	10	10
Second row	6, 7	5, 8	9, 4
Third row	3, 4, 8	2, 4, 9	2, 5, 8
Fourth row	1, 2, 5, 9	1, 3, 6, 7	1, 3, 6, 7

Let the children compare solutions, then compile a class set. These can be discussed and similarities explored.

For the extension activity, the numbers can be arranged as follows: 10
      6, 7
     8, 4, 3
    1, 9, 2, 5

Suggested questions:
● Do you think the top number always has to be the same?
● How did you work out what the top number should be?
● Have you found more than one solution?
● What is the difference between these solutions?

Digit sums (page 29)

☆ *Processes: look for pattern, explain, compare, be systematic, reason, check*

The grid should be completed in the following way:

1	2	3	4	5	6	7	8	9	1
2	3	4	5	6	7	8	9	10	2
3	4	5	6	7	8	9	10	11	3
4	5	6	7	8	9	10	11	12	4
5	6	7	8	9	10	11	12	13	5
6	7	8	9	10	11	12	13	14	6
7	8	9	10	11	12	13	14	15	7
8	9	10	11	12	13	14	15	16	8
9	10	11	12	13	14	15	16	17	9
10	11	12	13	14	15	16	17	18	1

Looking at the diagonals from bottom left to top right, the children should notice that the sum of the two-digit numbers is the same as the single-digit number in the last column of the grid.

Suggested questions/prompts:

● What patterns do you notice?
● Explain your thinking to your partner.

Pick 'n' mix: 1 and 2 (pages 30–31)

☆ *Processes: make decisions, ask own questions, record, explain, co-operate, look for pattern, be systematic*

Encourage discussion about the different masses of the sweets, using vocabulary such as 'heavier', 'heaviest', 'lighter', 'lightest'. If children find it too challenging to look at the total mass of three types of sweet, they could explore two types of sweet instead. With three types of sweet, it is possible to make all the masses that are multiples of 5 from 30 g to 120 g. There are only two ways of making exactly 100 g with three cards (50 g + 20 g + 30 g or 50 g + 40 g + 10 g).

Suggested questions:

● What totals have you made?
● Can you find another way of making the total 100 g? What other questions could you ask?
● How many different ways could you make exactly 80 g?

Guess if it's less (page 32)

☆ *Processes: estimate, predict, test ideas, compare*

Encourage the children to explain what they did when predicting which questions would have an answer of less than 15, and to compare their predictions with those of a partner.

Suggested questions:

● Which did you guess would be less than 15?
● What made you think that this one would have an answer less than 15?
● [Isla] ticked a question and then found that it had an answer of exactly 15. Was her guess correct?

Spot the difference (page 33)

☆ *Processes: look for pattern, predict, explain, reason, be systematic, generalise, test ideas, co-operate*

The children should notice that for odd numbers of cubes the differences will always be odd, and for even numbers of cubes the differences will always be even (including zero). Encourage the children to suggest reasons for the patterns they have discovered and to make predictions about other numbers. At the end of the lesson, form a general statement as a whole class. (The first sentence above demonstrates the process of generalising.)

Suggested questions/prompts:

● Explain to your partner what you notice.
● Why do you think this could be?
● How could you show what you have found on a poster?

Measures, shape and space

Letter trails: 1 and 2 (pages 34–35)

☆ *Processes: be systematic, check, predict, test ideas, look for pattern*

To introduce this activity, you could copy this diagram onto the board:

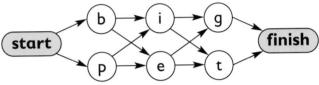

Demonstrate that eight different words can be made by moving from start to finish in different ways.

This activity develops the children's perseverance and encourages checking of solutions to ensure that the set is complete. To work out the number of different routes for each trail, multiply the number of letters in each column: for example, if there are three columns and two letters per column, this gives 8 solutions ($2 \times 2 \times 2 = 8$). On *Letter trails: 2*, the first trail has 12 routes ($3 \times 2 \times 2$) and the second trail has 9 ($3 \times 1 \times 3$).

Suggested questions:

● Have you found all the routes?
● How could you check?
● How many words have you made which start with b/f?

X marks the square (page 36)

☆ *Processes: trial and improvement, test ideas, record, reason, be systematic, explain, compare*

The children may begin to notice that, once one square has been marked with a cross, all the pieces can be rotated in the same arrangement to cross off three more squares. They will find that all the squares in the grid can be crossed. By recording their findings, focus can be made on being systematic. The children may also begin to appreciate how recording aids memory, as they may quickly forget how they found the solutions. Emphasise that recording is vital for showing others what you did, and as a personal reference that can be looked back on.

- Tell me what you noticed.
- Talk to a partner about what you did.
- What did you learn from this activity?

Chuckle the clown (page 37)

☆ *Processes: be systematic, visualise, look for pattern, check*

Since there are 3 wigs, 2 noses and 2 mouths, there are 12 different combinations ($3 \times 2 \times 2$). As a further extension, the children can be asked to add an extra nose and explore new combinations. This will give six more possibilities ($3 \times 3 \times 2 = 18$ combinations in total).

The extension activity helps the children to check that all their clown faces are different, since each should make a different word. The words are: RAT, BAT, PAT, RUT, BUT, PUT, RAN, BAN, PAN, RUN, BUN, PUN.

Suggested questions:
- How is this clown you have drawn different from this one?
- What if these clowns changed their noses? How many more clowns could you draw?
- What word does this clown make?
- Have you found 12 different words?

Secret shapes (page 38)

☆ *Processes: visualise, compare, reason*

This activity helps the children to appreciate that the hidden part of a shape can take on a range of different forms and not just the expected shape. The children may not be able to name all their four-sided shapes unless they are familiar with the term 'quadrilateral'. As an alternative to the extension activity suggested in the Teachers' note at the foot of the sheet, the children could cut three or four identical shapes from coloured paper and cover a different part of each shape with a piece of paper, asking a partner: 'These shapes are all identical. Can you guess what shape they are?' These can form lively displays and encourage the children to visualise and notice properties of shapes.

Suggested questions/prompts:
- Can you imagine what this shape might look like?
- How many sides do you think it might have?
- What shape have you drawn?
- Are there other shapes you could have drawn?
- Tell us about your shapes.

Timetables and rotas: 1 and 2
(pages 39–40)

☆ *Processes: record, make decisions, explain, ask own questions*

It is not expected that the children reproduce accurate timetables or rotas, but that they should be given experience of recording things that happen or should happen at particular times or on particular days. This will help them to become aware of the importance of committing things to paper as an aid to memory, and will encourage them to think about effective ways of showing such information. Discuss these things when showing the tables from *Timetables and rotas: 1* and any others specific to your classroom. Ensure the children understand that they can choose what they would like to show on their own chart. They could make a timetable of things that they do each day (such as get up, breakfast, school, TV…) or they could allocate classroom responsibilities to groups within the class. Giving the activity purpose in the classroom setting will make the activity more meaningful. Encourage the children to explain their charts to others (in pairs or small groups) and, as a class, draw attention to original or unusual approaches.

Suggested questions/prompts:
- What did you decide to show on your chart?
- How did you record this? Explain it to us.
- What questions could you ask about [Jack]'s chart?
- Look at what [Connor] did. Can you explain it to us?

Wriggling worms (page 41)

☆ *Processes: estimate, predict, test ideas, visualise*

Discuss strategies for gaining a sense of how long each worm is, such as using fingers to estimate the number of centimetres. Show the children how to test their estimates by placing string carefully along each worm and then marking the ends, before pulling the string straight and measuring it against a ruler. The correct order of the worms is B, F, D, C, E, A.

Approximate lengths are:
A = 31 cm, B = 13 cm, C = 25 cm, D = 20 cm,
E = 29 cm, F = 16 cm

Suggested questions:
- Which worm do you think is longest/shortest?
- How could you check your estimates?
- How close were your estimates?

Mystery tour (page 42)

☆ *Processes: make decisions, visualise, record, estimate, co-operate, test ideas*

When the children write their own tours, ensure that they test them out several times to check that they have not missed anything or made a mistake. This activity can be expanded to include any number of instructions and places around the school. Encourage the children to end the tour facing something distinct, such as a sink or poster.

Suggested questions:
- Where do you end up?
- Could we use metres instead of paces?
- What other tours could we make?

Spinning around (page 43)

☆ *Processes: look for pattern, reason, predict, visualise, test ideas, explain, generalise*

Here, the children use a cut-out arrow and dial to explore the effects of turning the arrow through odd and even numbers of quarter turns. Encourage discussion of what the children have found and, at the end of the lesson, compose generalised statements: for example, 'The arrow always ends on A when the number of quarter turns is a multiple of 4. An odd number of quarter turns always ends on B or D'. The children can then predict other outcomes and test their ideas practically.

- What do you notice?
- Can you think of any other numbers of quarter turns that might get you back to A?
- Can you explain why you think that might be?
- Can we make up a true sentence about what we have found out?

Balancing act (page 44)

☆ *Processes: trial and improvement, test ideas, compare, co-operate, be systematic, visualise*

This sheet could be used as an introductory activity leading on to other similar investigations, such as:

- 'What is the most number of cubes you can add to this model, if only one cube can touch the table and the model must not fall over or grow any taller?'

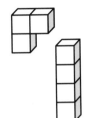

- 'How many cubes tall can we make a stick without it falling over?'

- 'What if we make a stick five cubes high and add one cube to the side of the top cube. Does it balance? What if we now add another cube? What if the stick was six cubes tall?'

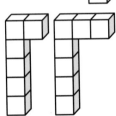

Suggested questions:
- What have you found out?
- Do you think you have found all the places?
- Did you work well together?
- What other things could we explore?

Spot the shape (page 45)

☆ *Processes: explain, co-operate, make decisions, look for pattern, visualise, compare, reason*

For the extension activity suggested in the Teachers' note at the foot of the sheet, there are no right or wrong ways of sorting the shapes. Some children may collect together shapes with curved sides or straight sides or both, while others may use different criteria, such as having a circle and a triangle or shapes with two lines crossing. The emphasis should be on explaining the features of the shapes and the reasons for sorting in a particular way. Through working with a partner, co-operation skills are also explored. Ask each pair to explain their sorting to the others in the class and discuss differences between the pairs' ideas.

Suggested questions:
- How many curved/straight lines does this shape have?
- Can you explain how you sorted the shapes?
- Why did you put this shape here?
- Did anyone else sort theirs in a similar way?
- How many shapes have you put in this group?
- Did you have a shape in a group on its own? Why?

Jigsaw: 1 and 2 (pages 46–47)

☆ *Processes: trial and improvement, reason, record, ask own questions, be systematic, visualise*

This activity can be tackled with the whole class, or children can work individually or in pairs. There is a range of solutions, including the following:

Corner pieces: A, C, J, L
Side pieces: B, D, F, G, I, K
Middle pieces: E, H
Same shape: G, K

Examples of rectangles:

A	B	C
D	E	F
G	H	I
J	K	L

plus the same, but with G and K swapped

plus these solutions upside down

A	D	J
G	H	K
F	E	B
C	I	L

plus the same, but with G and K swapped

plus these solutions upside down

Examples of squares:

A	J
C	L

A	D	J
G	H	I
L	B	C

(G and K interchangeable)

C	D	A
I	H	B
J	G	L

(G and K interchangeable)

Example of a straight line:

J	K	F	D	G	I	B	A

Suggested questions:
- Did you find this hard? Why do you think that was?
- What other things could we explore?

Shape sequences (page 48)

☆ *Processes: visualise, reason, make decisions, look for pattern, compare, explain, co-operate*

This activity can lead on to a wide range of extension work where children create their own sequence cards for others to arrange.

Suggested questions/prompts:
- Why did you choose to arrange them like this?
- What did you notice?
- Can you explain your thinking?
- Now try making up your own sequence.
- Swap cards with a partner.

Number maker

• **Use these number names to make as many numbers as you can.**

Write the words **and** the numbers.

seventy	nine
twenty	seven
eighty	two

seventy-nine 79

1. How many numbers did you make? _____

2. How many:

   (a) have the digit 2? ____   **(b)** have the digit 8? ____

   (c) have two digits the same? ____   **(d)** are even? ____

   (e) are greater than 50? ____   **(f)** are odd? ____

• **What if you could also use** fifty **?**

How many more numbers could you make?

Teachers' note In this activity the children practise reading and writing numbers in words and figures in an open way. The children are likely to ask whether they can include single numbers such as 80 and 2. Encourage them to make their own decision, as this will help to steer them away from the idea that there is only one correct way of doing things.

Developing Numeracy
Using & Applying Maths
Year 2
© A & C BLACK

Hearty puzzles

Reason and generalise

☆ Use the digits **2** **3** **4** **4** **6** **8** to make three numbers between 10 and 99. **Example:** 84 24 36

☆ Draw a circle around the **largest** number.

☆ Draw a square around the **smallest** number.

☆ Draw a heart around the number that lies **between**.

• **Find as many heart numbers as you can.**

_____   _____   _____

_____   _____   _____

_____   _____   _____

_____   _____   _____

_____   _____   _____

• **Record your heart numbers here.**

36

How many heart numbers:

(a) did you find? _____

(b) begin with **2** or **8**? _____

(c) include a **2** or an **8**? _____

 • **Choose six digits which are all different. Do the same again.**

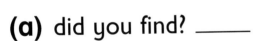

Teachers' note To investigate how many 'heart numbers' can be made, the children should compare findings and make a group list. When looking at which of the numbers include the digits 2 and 8, encourage them to notice that these are the lowest and highest digits of the set. As a further extension, the children could examine the possibilities for numbers in the circle or the square.

Developing Numeracy Using & Applying Maths Year 2 © A & C BLACK

Seating plan

Reason and look for patterns

- **Ring all the** multiples of 3 **on each block of seats.**

13	14	15
10	11	12
7	8	9
4	5	6
1	2	3

3 seats per row

17	18	19	20
13	14	15	16
9	10	11	12
5	6	7	8
1	2	3	4

4 seats per row

25	26	27	28	29	30
19	20	21	22	23	24
13	14	15	16	17	18
7	8	9	10	11	12
1	2	3	4	5	6

6 seats per row

9	10
7	8
5	6
3	4
1	2

2 seats per row

21	22	23	24	25
16	17	18	19	20
11	12	13	14	15
6	7	8	9	10
1	2	3	4	5

5 seats per row

29	30	31	32	33	34	35
22	23	24	25	26	27	28
15	16	17	18	19	20	21
8	9	10	11	12	13	14
1	2	3	4	5	6	7

7 seats per row

There are three patterns:

 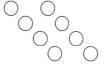

- **Write the number of seats per row under the correct pattern.**

2, _____ _____ _____

- Predict **the patterns for** 8 **,** 9 **and** 10 **seats per row.**
- **Find out if you were right.**

Now try this!

Teachers' note If necessary, provide a list of multiples of 3 on the board. Encourage the children to describe what they notice to a partner and to use vocabulary such as 'straight lines' and 'diagonal patterns'. Ask them to say why they think some blocks show one type of pattern and others another, and draw attention to the number of seats in each row of the block.

Developing Numeracy
Using & Applying Maths
Year 2
© A & C BLACK

Halfway house

- **On each number line, write numbers in the circles which have a** difference of 10 **.**

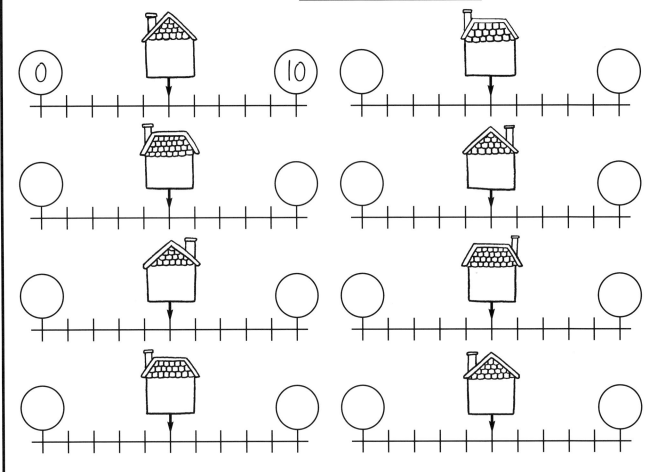

- **Fill in the number on the halfway house.**

- **Add the circle numbers on each number line, then halve the answer. What do you notice?**

_____

Now try this!

- **Write four pairs of numbers with a** difference of 20 **. Find the halfway house numbers. What do you notice?**

Teachers' note Begin the lesson by counting in tens from any number, and draw attention to the fact that pairs of numbers in the counting sequence have a difference of ten. In this activity the children can choose any numbers that they feel comfortable with that have a difference of ten. Rather than teaching a strategy for finding the halfway number, allow the children to explore ways themselves.

Developing Numeracy Using & Applying Maths Year 2 © A & C BLACK

Fair shares

- **Work with a partner.**

  These packets hold an

  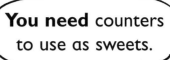

  | even | **number of sweets.**

- **Share each packet equally with your partner.**

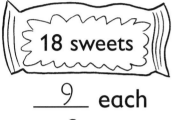

____9____ each

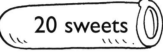

_____ each

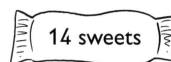

_____ each

_____ each

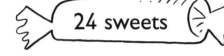

_____ each

_____ each

These packets hold an | odd | **number of sweets.**

- **Share each packet between you.**

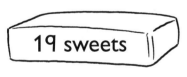

_____ each

_____ each

_____ each

- **What do you notice?** _____

_____

- **Make a poster about sharing odd and even numbers of sweets between two people.**

Teachers' note This activity helps the children to appreciate that when sharing an odd number of sweets, either a sweet must be split in half, or there will be one sweet left over. Encourage the children to verbalise this in their own way. Each pair will need 30 counters to represent sweets. For the extension activity, give each pair of children a large sheet of paper and ask them to make a poster which will help others to understand what they have found out.

Developing Numeracy
Using & Applying Maths
Year 2
© A & C BLACK

An odd puzzle

Use trial and improvement, and test your ideas

⊙ ☆ Place a counter on **start**.

☆ Move it along the lines to the finish.
Every time you reach an **odd** number,
you lose a cube.

☆ Try different routes. What is the most
cubes you can have left at the finish?

You need:
• a counter
• five cubes

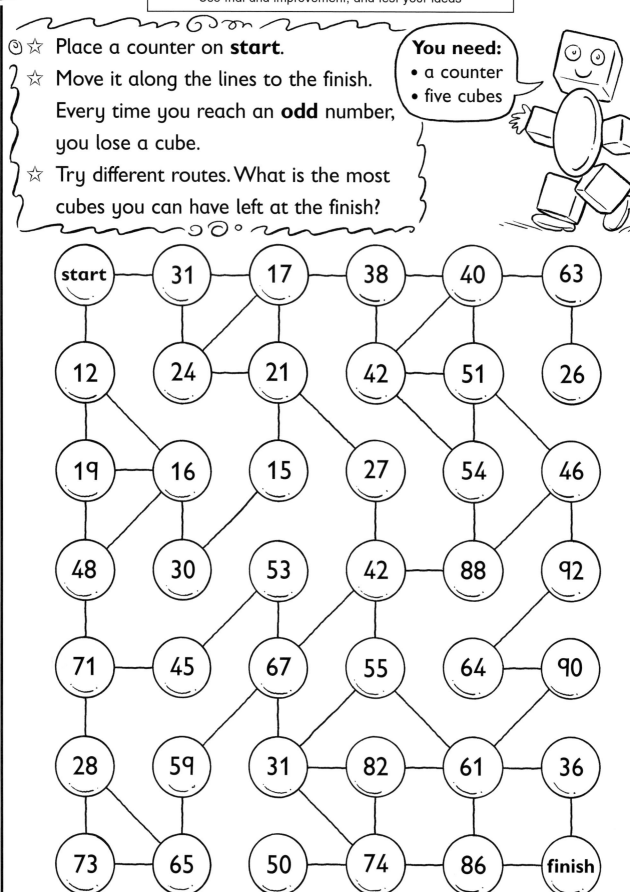

Teachers' note This activity helps the children to develop perseverance. Each child will need a counter and five cubes. Encourage them to try the puzzle again and again, using different routes. They may find it helpful to use coloured pencils to mark routes they have tried. They might also find it easier if they write E or O (even or odd) next to each number, to make it quicker when searching for routes.

Developing Numeracy
Using & Applying Maths
Year 2
© A & C BLACK

Months of the year

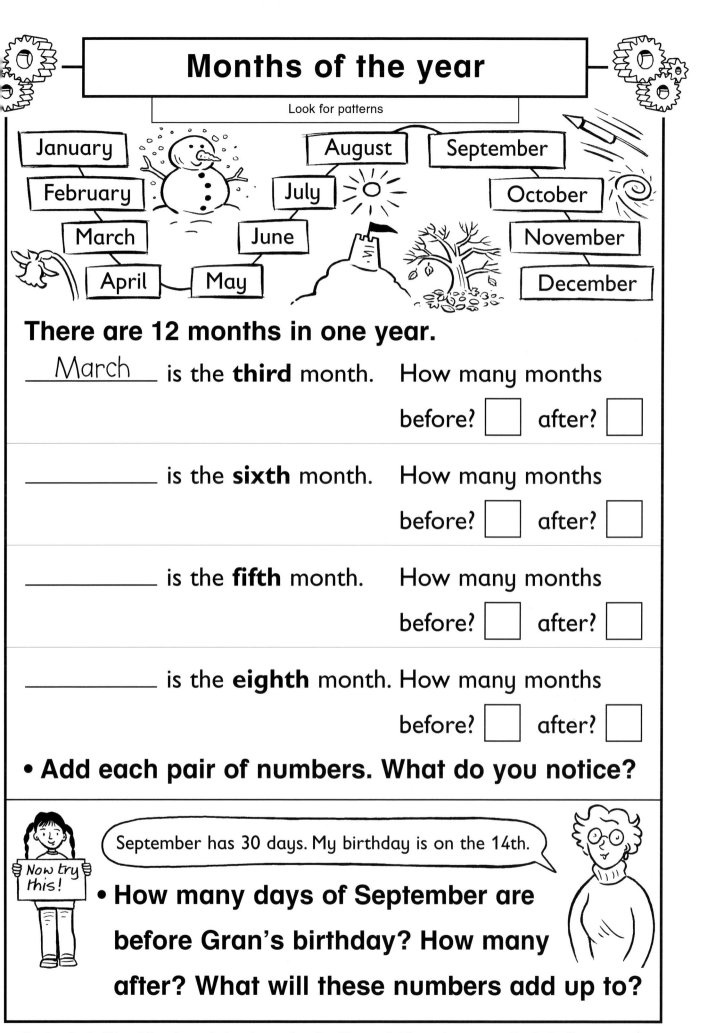

January February March April May June July August September October November December

There are 12 months in one year.

March is the **third** month. How many months before? ☐ after? ☐

_____ is the **sixth** month. How many months before? ☐ after? ☐

_____ is the **fifth** month. How many months before? ☐ after? ☐

_____ is the **eighth** month. How many months before? ☐ after? ☐

• **Add each pair of numbers. What do you notice?**

September has 30 days. My birthday is on the 14th.

• **How many days of September are before Gran's birthday? How many after? What will these numbers add up to?**

Now try this!

Teachers' note This activity revises ordinal numbers and months of the year, but the most important idea is for the children to look for patterns in their answers and to try to explain what they notice. Begin by revising the months of the year and discussing ordinal numbers (for example, first, seventh, twelfth). At the end of the lesson, talk through the activity as a class and discuss the totals produced.

**Developing Numeracy
Using & Applying Maths
Year 2
© A & C BLACK**

Don't bug me!

Co-operate and make estimates

• **Work with a partner.**

> **You each need** a copy of this sheet.

☆ Choose a leaf.
  Both estimate the number of bugs on that leaf.

☆ Count to check. Group the bugs in fives to help you.

☆ Score a point if your estimate was closer.

☆ The winner is the player with the most points.

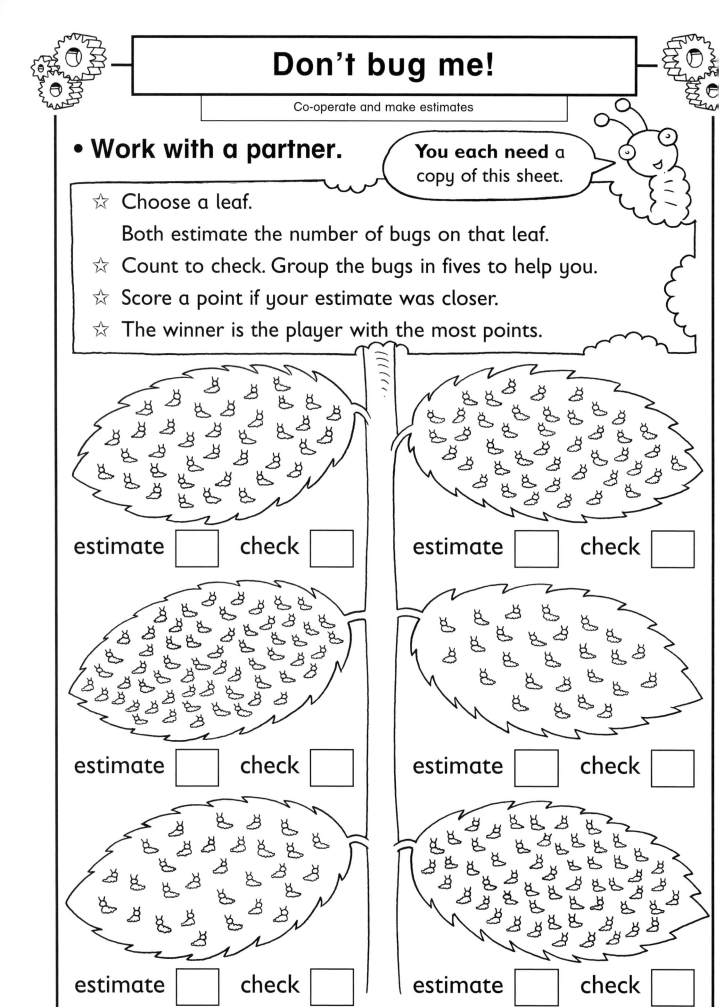

estimate ☐ check ☐

estimate ☐ check ☐

estimate ☐ check ☐

estimate ☐ check ☐

estimate ☐ check ☐

estimate ☐ check ☐

Teachers' note At the start of the lesson, discuss ways of counting a large number of items, including strategies for helping you not to lose count, such as drawing a ring around five of the items at a time. Practise counting in fives up to 50 and beyond. Encourage both children in the pair to count the bugs on the leaf to establish the correct number. As an extension, ask the children to draw bugs on a leaf for a partner to estimate.

Developing Numeracy
Using & Applying Maths
Year 2
© A & C BLACK

Changing groups

Be systematic and look for patterns

Six children need to get into groups.
There must be more than one group.
A child <u>can</u> be on his or her own in
a group.

• Find ten ways to put the children into groups.

• 1	•• 3	• • 2		• 1	• 1	• • 2	• • 2

• How many ways have you found where there are:

2 groups?   3 groups?   4 groups?   5 groups?   6 groups?

☐   ☐   ☐   ☐   ☐

• Write all your ways in order,

starting with 2 groups.

Write the smallest number first.

1 5,

_____

_____

What if there were seven children?

• Find 14 ways to put them into groups.

Teachers' note Begin by asking five children to come to the front of the class. Explain that the five children must get into groups and that groups can have only one child. First record different ways of putting them into two groups, i.e. 1 4 and 2 3. Explain that 3 2 is the same as 2 3. Then explore ways of putting them into three groups, four groups and finally five groups. See page 8 for solutions to the activity sheet. Encourage systematic working and allow the children to discuss their findings.

Developing Numeracy
Using & Applying Maths
Year 2
© A & C BLACK

Nine planets

Look for patterns and compare

Nine planets are numbered $\boxed{1}$ to $\boxed{9}$.

• Draw lines to join planets with:

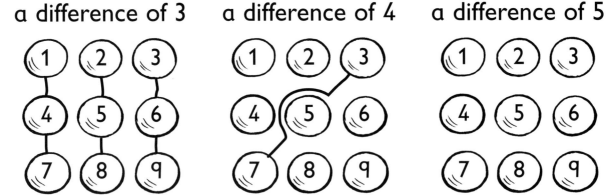

a difference of 3   a difference of 4   a difference of 5

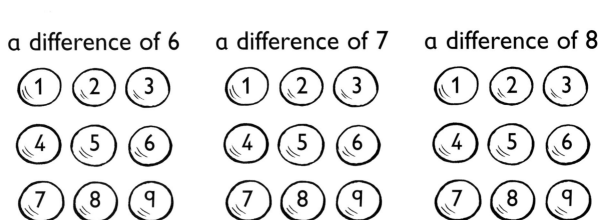

a difference of 6   a difference of 7   a difference of 8

• How many lines did you draw for a difference of:

3? $\boxed{6}$ 4? $\boxed{}$ 5? $\boxed{}$ 6? $\boxed{}$ 7? $\boxed{}$ 8? $\boxed{}$

• Talk to a partner about what you notice.

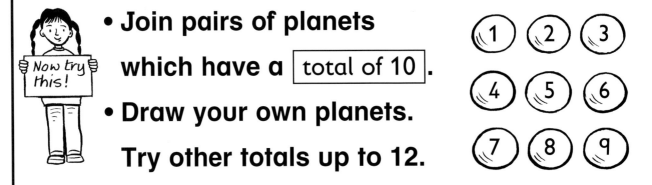

Now try this!

• **Join pairs of planets which have a** $\boxed{\text{total of 10}}$.

• **Draw your own planets. Try other totals up to 12.**

Teachers' note This activity encourages the children to explore and compare different patterns made by lines when joining numbers with particular differences or totals. Show the children how looking for patterns can help them to check that they have found all the solutions: for example, if one line is missed on the 'difference of 5' diagram, then the pattern of lines would be 6, 5, **3**, 3, 2, 1, drawing attention to a missing line.

Developing Numeracy
Using & Applying Maths
Year 2
© A & C BLACK

Supermarket challenge

Reason and use trial and improvement

• Try this challenge.

☆ Go through the supermarket to the checkout. When you pass an item, you must put it in your trolley.

☆ Try to reach the checkout with exactly **£30** of shopping in your trolley. Draw the route you have found.

Use a coloured pencil.

£3 magazine £1 cereal chips £3 £3 £10

£5 Recipes £9 £1 £9

£1 £7 £5 £2 £5

£1 £2 £3 £6 £1

in checkout

• Ask questions of your own, like these. Then answer them.

Now try this!

What is the smallest total you could pay at the checkout?

What is the smallest number of items you could buy?

Teachers' note This activity encourages the children to use trial and improvement strategies initially, and then to begin reasoning (see pages 8–9). Such reasoning is at the heart of solving problems like this, as it helps to narrow down the options. Explain to the children that every item they pass must be put in the trolley, and that their route must not jump across the supermarket aisles except where there is a gap. They will need coloured pencils, and paper for jottings.

Developing Numeracy
Using & Applying Maths
Year 2
© A & C BLACK

Mystery money

Three children have a coin each.

It could be 1p , 2p or 5p .

- **There are ten totals they could have. Find them all.**

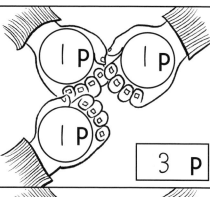

3 P

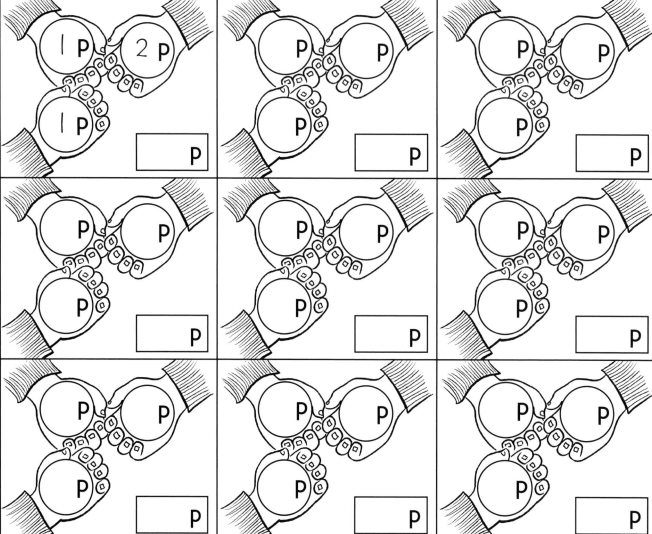

1p 2p 1p — ___ P	P P P — ___ P	P P P — ___ P
P P P — ___ P	P P P — ___ P	P P P — ___ P
P P P — ___ P	P P P — ___ P	P P P — ___ P

Now try this!

- **This time the coins could be**

  1p , 2p , 5p or 10p .

- **Find all the totals.**

Teachers' note Provide each child with three 1p, three 2p and three 5p coins. Discuss ways of working systematically (see page 9) and point out that the order does not matter: for example, 1p, 1p and 5p is the same as 5p, 1p and 1p. Encourage the children to compare their solutions with a partner, then compile a class list of solutions on the board. Ask: 'How many solutions use a 1p/2p/5p coin?' Show that looking for patterns can help to check solutions.

Developing Numeracy
Using & Applying Maths
Year 2
© A & C BLACK

24

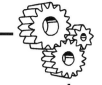

Switch the units

- **These children make** two-digit numbers **from place value cards. Find the total of each pair.**

2 5   1 3   _38_

3 4   1 2

1 6   2 1

1 8   4 1

1 7   3 2

2 3   1 9

The children in each pair swap units digits.

- **Complete the numbers and find their totals.**

2 3   1 5

3 1

1   2

1   4

1   3

2   1

Now try this!

- **Write pairs of** three-digit numbers .

   Find the totals.

- **Swap the units digits.**

   Is the total the same?

2 4 2

5 3 4

Teachers' note At the start of the lesson, discuss suitable strategies for finding the totals, such as counting on, partitioning, or adding the nearest multiple of 10 and adjusting. Encourage the children to suggest reasons for the totals being the same and to write other pairs of additions that will have the same totals. As a further extension, ask: 'What if we swapped the tens or hundreds digits of two numbers?'

**Developing Numeracy
Using & Applying Maths
Year 2
© A & C BLACK**

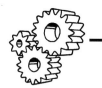

Trailer tricks

Look for patterns and be systematic

As the lorry goes under the bridges, the numbers on the trailer change.

• **Follow the instructions on the bridges. Write the finish numbers on the garages.**

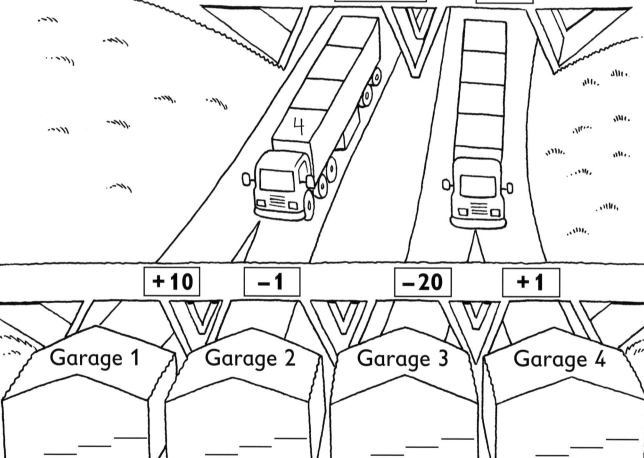

• **Look at the numbers on each garage. Explain to a partner the patterns you notice.**

• **Try different trailer numbers to test your ideas.**

Teachers' note Explain to the children that they should carry out the instruction for each number on the trailer. Note that if 1 is used as a trailer number, it will produce a negative number on Garage 3. As an extension, the children could write different instructions on the bridges and explore the outcome (using a copy of this sheet with the instructions on the bridges masked). Interesting number patterns are often produced, particularly when numbers are doubled, halved or multiplied by 10.

Developing Numeracy Using & Applying Maths Year 2 © A & C BLACK

Dial a word

On some phones, the buttons show numbers **and** letters.

To find a word total, add the numbers for each letter.

Example:

p h o n e
7 + 4 + 6 + 6 + 3 = 26

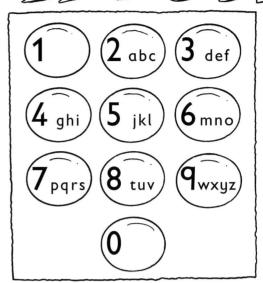

• **Choose one of these topics and tick it.**

• **Find the totals for six words on your topic.**

What words can I find?   What questions can I ask?

_____

_____

_____

_____

_____

Teachers' note This activity has been designed to be open-ended, so that the children can make their own decisions about directions to explore. When looking for words, encourage them to ask their own questions: for example, 'Which is the largest/smallest total? Which total is nearest to 20? Can I find two words with the same total?' As an extension, ask the children to make a poster showing the words and totals, and the questions that they asked (see page 9).

**Developing Numeracy
Using & Applying Maths
Year 2
© A & C BLACK**

Playing pool

Reason and use trial and improvement

The pool balls are numbered 1 to 10.

• **Try to arrange the balls so that each row adds up to the number shown. Find different ways.**

Cross out ways that do not work.

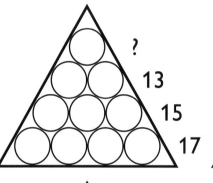

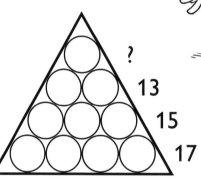

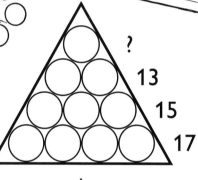

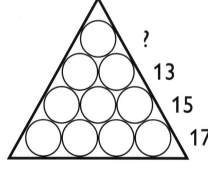

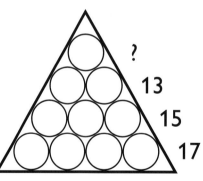

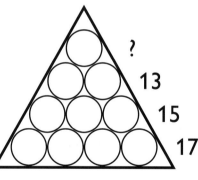

• **Explain to a partner what you notice.**

Now try this!

• **Arrange the balls so that the rows and diagonals add up to these numbers.**

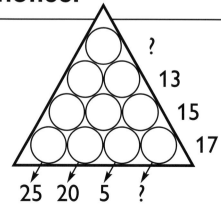

Teachers' note Point out that each ball can only be used once. Encourage the children to record and cross out ways that do not work, and then to spend some time thinking and describe what they have found out: for example, 'I have worked out what the top number must be since I know that all the other rows add up to 45.' As a further extension, the children could arrange the balls to make different row totals, and set puzzles of their own for a partner to solve.

**Developing Numeracy
Using & Applying Maths
Year 2
© A & C BLACK**

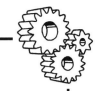

Digit sums

Look for patterns and explain your findings

• **For each number, find the sum of the digits.**

25 → 2 + 5 = 7   37 → 3 + 7 = _____   22 → _____

48 → _____   62 → _____   87 → _____

• **Try other numbers between 10 and 100.**

_____   _____   _____

_____   _____   _____

• **Look at the numbers in the hundred square.**

☆ Find the sum of the digits in each number. Write it in the new grid.

☆ What patterns do you notice? Talk to your partner.

1	2	3	4	5	6	7	8	9	10
11	12	13	14	15	16	17	18	19	20
21	22	23	24	25	26	27	28	29	30
31	32	33	34	35	36	37	38	39	40
41	42	43	44	45	46	47	48	49	50
51	52	53	54	55	56	57	58	59	60
61	62	63	64	65	66	67	68	69	70
71	72	73	74	75	76	77	78	79	80
81	82	83	84	85	86	87	88	89	90
91	92	93	94	95	96	97	98	99	100

1	2	3	4	5	6	7	8	9	1
				7					
4									
								13	

Now try this!

• **Look at the** two-digit numbers **in your new grid. Find the sum of the digits.**

Talk to a partner about what you notice.

Teachers' note The children should work in pairs or small groups for this activity, to encourage discussion of the patterns. Draw out that spotting patterns can save a lot of time and can also help when checking answers. Ensure the children understand that for each number in the hundred square, they should write the sum of the digits in the corresponding square of the new grid.

**Developing Numeracy
Using & Applying Maths
Year 2
© A & C BLACK**

Pick 'n' mix: 1

Make decisions and ask your own questions

You need the cards from *Pick 'n' mix: 2.*

☆ Pick three cards.

☆ How much do the sweets weigh altogether? Use the number line to help you. Start at zero and jump up in fives or tens.

☆ Do it again. How many different totals can you find?

20 g + 30 g + 15 g = 65 g

- **Work with a partner. Answer these questions.**

Now try this!

My sweets weigh 100 g in total. Which three cards could I have?

I have three cards. What is the most the sweets could weigh?

| 120 g |
| 115 g |
| 110 g |
| 105 g |
| 100 g |
| 95 g |
| 90 g |
| 85 g |
| 80 g |
| 75 g |
| 70 g |
| 65 g |
| 60 g |
| 55 g |
| 50 g |
| 45 g |
| 40 g |
| 35 g |
| 30 g |
| 25 g |
| 20 g |
| 15 g |
| 10 g |
| 5 g |
| 0 g |

Teachers' note The children will need copies of page 31. At the start of the lesson, demonstrate how to use the number line to find totals, and ensure the children are familiar with the unit of grams. When the children are talking to each other about their choices, encourage them to ask and answer their own questions: for example, 'How many different ways can I make the total 60 g?'

**Developing Numeracy
Using & Applying Maths
Year 2
© A & C BLACK**

30

Pick 'n' mix: 2

• **Cut out the cards.**

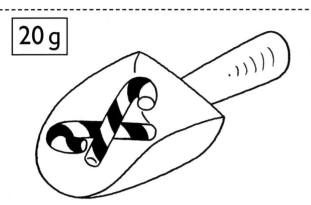

20 g

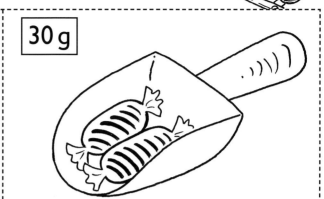

30 g

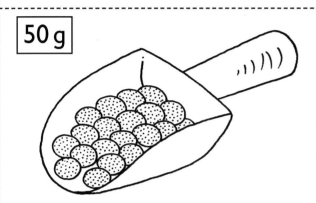

50 g

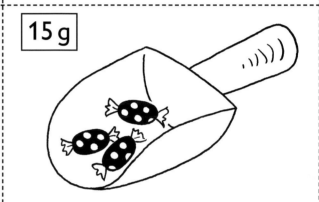

15 g

25 g

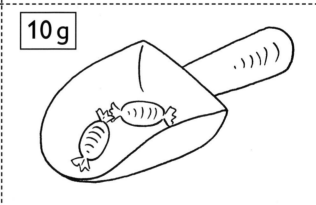

10 g

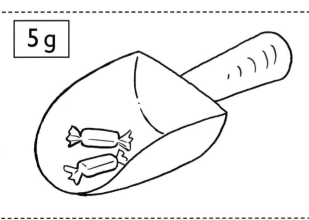

5 g

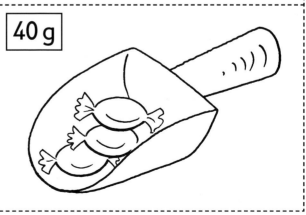

40 g

Teachers' note These cards should be cut out and used with page 30. The cards could be laminated to create a more permanent resource for use in informal play and role play, or for whole class games.

**Developing Numeracy
Using & Applying Maths
Year 2
© A & C BLACK**

Guess if it's less

Make estimates and predictions

• **Tick the questions which you think will have an answer that is** | less than 15 |.

You have 1 minute.

7 + 3 ✔	9 + 10	7 + 7
19 – 2	20 – 14	19 + 1
11 + 2	8 + 6	10 + 9
20 – 8	21 – 4	19 – 9
7 + 8	2 + 12	8 + 8
17 – 5	24 – 10	17 – 9

• **Were you right? Find the totals to check.**

Now try this!

• **Work with a partner.**

☆ Write ten addition and subtraction questions.
☆ Swap with your partner.
☆ Predict which answers will be **less than 17**.
☆ Check to see if you were right.

Teachers' note Ensure the children realise that they should predict which answers will be less than 15 *without* working out the answers, and that they will have one minute to make their predictions. Use a timer and give instructions to start and stop. If necessary, provide apparatus or number lines for the children to use when checking their predictions. You could ask them to use a different-coloured pencil for checking, to ensure that predictions are not adjusted later on.

**Developing Numeracy
Using & Applying Maths
Year 2
© A & C BLACK**

Spot the difference

Look for patterns and make predictions

You need some cubes.

1. ☆ Make two sticks using exactly **11** cubes.
  ☆ Find the difference between the number of cubes in each stick.
  ☆ Write all the differences you can find, using <u>all</u> 11 cubes.

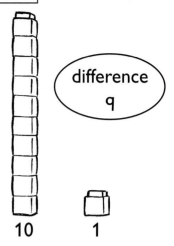

difference
9

10   1

difference
9

difference

difference

difference

difference

What do you notice? _____

2. Do the same thing with **10** cubes.

difference

difference

difference

difference

difference

What do you notice? _____

3. Predict the differences for exactly **12** cubes.

difference

difference

difference

difference

difference

difference

Find out if you were right.

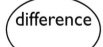

• **With a partner, make a poster to show what you have found out.**

Try other numbers of cubes.

Teachers' note The children will need 12 interlocking cubes each. Ensure that they understand the meaning of the word 'difference' and know how to find it. When the children are designing and making their poster for the extension activity, they could record the sticks they made by colouring squares on squared paper (preferably 2 cm × 2 cm squares). Encourage them to write explanations of the odd and even patterns they discovered.

**Developing Numeracy
Using & Applying Maths
Year 2
© A & C BLACK**

Letter trails: 1

There are eight routes from `start` to `finish`.

• Follow different routes.

• Write the letters as you go, to spell a word.

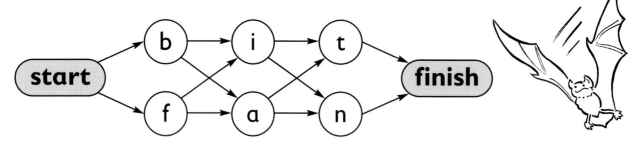

bat			

• Do the same with this trail.

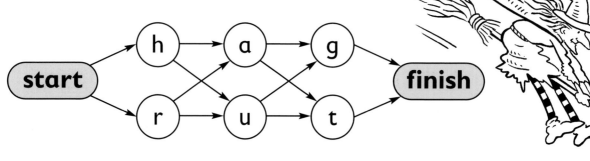

hag			

• Try this trail.

All the words end in **e**.

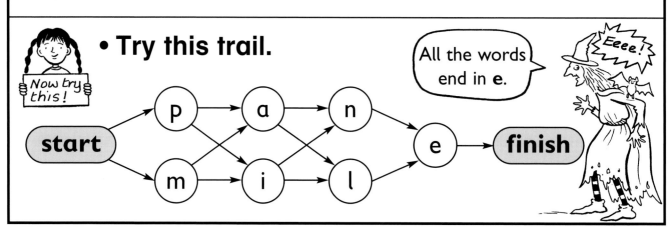

Teachers' note While this might look at first glance like a language activity, the ability to explore and find all possibilities is an important process for using and applying maths. Ensure the children understand that they must go from start to finish, and not use the letters randomly. Coloured pencils could be used to mark each different route. The children should be encouraged to check their solutions carefully. Ask them to collaborate and compare with a partner.

Developing Numeracy
Using & Applying Maths
Year 2
© A & C BLACK

Letter trails: 2

Make predictions and test your ideas

- **How many different routes do you <u>think</u> there are from** start **to** finish **?** ⬜

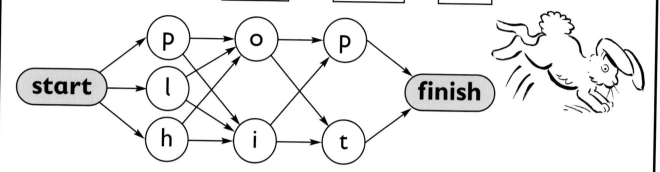

- **Find out if you were right. List the words on a separate piece of paper.**

- **Predict the number of routes for this trail.**

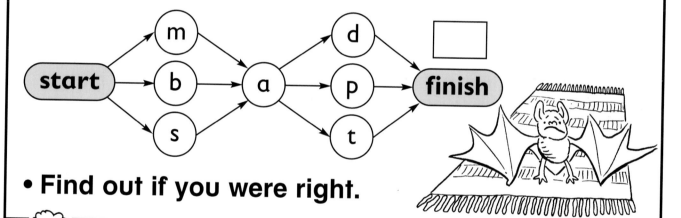

- **Find out if you were right.**

- **Predict the number of routes for these trails.**

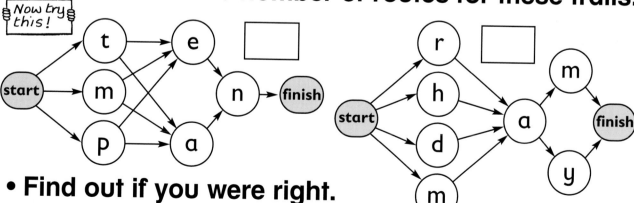

- **Find out if you were right.**

Teachers' note The children should first complete the activity on page 34, so that they understand what is being asked of them here. More confident children could try to devise their own simple trails, although the letters they choose may not result in a complete set of real words. This could be explored through questions such as: 'Which of your routes spell real words and which do not? Can you make a trail with more real words in? Which letters could you change?'

Developing Numeracy
Using & Applying Maths
Year 2
© A & C BLACK

X marks the square

Use trial and improvement, test your ideas and record

• Follow these instructions.

☆ Cut out the shapes below.

☆ Arrange them on this grid so that only one small square is uncovered.

☆ Mark the uncovered square with a cross.

☆ Try different ways. Find out which squares can be marked with a cross.

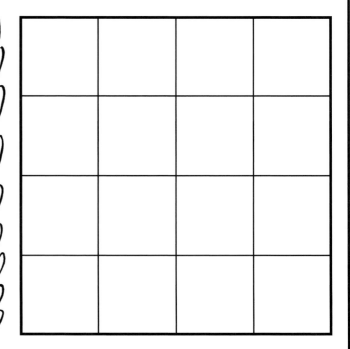

• Explain to a partner what you have found out.

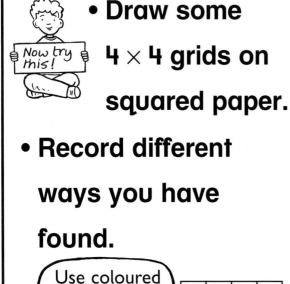

Now try this!

• Draw some 4 × 4 grids on squared paper.

• Record different ways you have found.

Use coloured pencils.

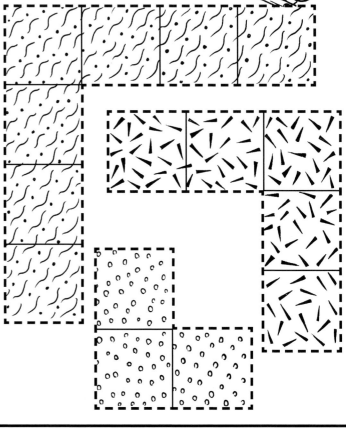

Teachers' note The children will need squared paper and coloured pencils for the extension activity. Encourage them to discuss and compare their work with others and to collaborate to find all the squares that can be marked with a cross (see pages 10–11). They will probably notice that there is often more than one way to arrange the pieces for a particular crossed square. Provide 4 × 4 grids already drawn on squared paper for less confident children.

Developing Numeracy
Using & Applying Maths
Year 2
© A & C BLACK

Chuckle the clown

Be systematic

Chuckle the clown has:

| 3 wigs | 2 noses | 2 mouths |

• **Draw** 12 **different pictures of Chuckle.**

 **Each wig, nose and mouth has a letter.**

  R   B   P   A   U   T   N

• **What word does each clown make?**

Write the word beneath the picture.

Teachers' note Some children might find it helpful to colour in each wig, nose and mouth in a
different colour. For the extension activity, the wig, nose and mouth chosen for each clown will spell
out a word, if the letters are written in that order: for example, the first clown spells out the word
'RAT'. The investigation can be extended by adding an extra nose (see page 11).

**Developing Numeracy
Using & Applying Maths
Year 2
© A & C BLACK**

Secret shapes

- **Part of a shape is hidden.**

  It has ⬜3⬜, ⬜4⬜, ⬜5⬜ or ⬜6⬜ **straight sides.**

  What could the shape be?

- **Draw a different shape each time.**

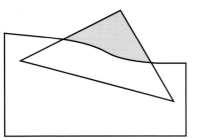 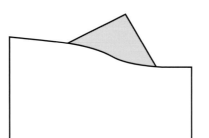 

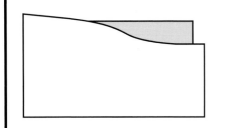 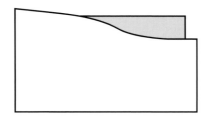 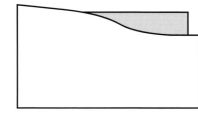

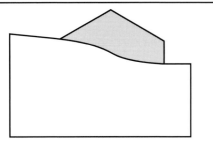 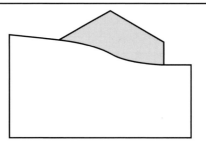 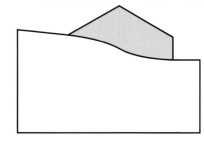

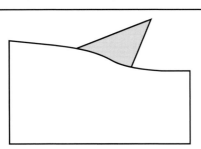 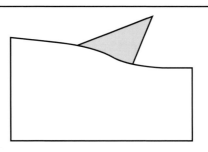 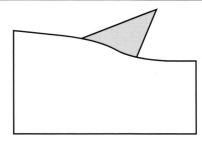

- **Write the name of each shape, if you can.**

Teachers' note Emphasise that the children must draw straight lines and make a shape with up to six sides. Encourage them to imagine that the lines continue behind the screen, rather than assuming that the points touching the edge of the screen are vertices of the shape. Demonstrate this idea with the whole class, using plastic shapes and paper. Introduce or revise 'pentagon' and 'hexagon'. As an extension, the children could draw some partly hidden shapes of their own.

**Developing Numeracy
Using & Applying Maths
Year 2
© A & C BLACK**

38

Timetables and rotas: 1

Record and make decisions

	9:00		10:30	12:00	1:00		3:15
Monday	A S S E M B L Y	Maths	P L A Y T I M E	English	Lunch	PE	Art
Tuesday		Maths		English	Lunch	Science	History
Wednesday		Maths		English	Lunch	Geography	
Thursday		Maths		English	Lunch	Games	Music
Friday		Maths		English	Lunch	Science	

	Tidying up	**Pencil sharpening**	**Taking messages**
Group A	Monday	Wednesday	Friday
Group B	Tuesday	Thursday	Monday
Group C	Wednesday	Friday	Tuesday
Group D	Thursday	Monday	Wednesday
Group E	Friday	Tuesday	Thursday

Teachers' note This sheet should be enlarged and used as an introduction to the activity on page 40. Discuss that people use timetables and rotas so that they know what they should be doing at a particular time or on a particular day. This might be for classroom jobs, or to tell them what lesson they should be doing. Discuss the charts, and any other timetables that the children will be able to relate to, then give each child a copy of page 40 to complete.

Developing Numeracy
Using & Applying Maths
Year 2
© A & C BLACK

Timetables and rotas: 2

Record and make decisions

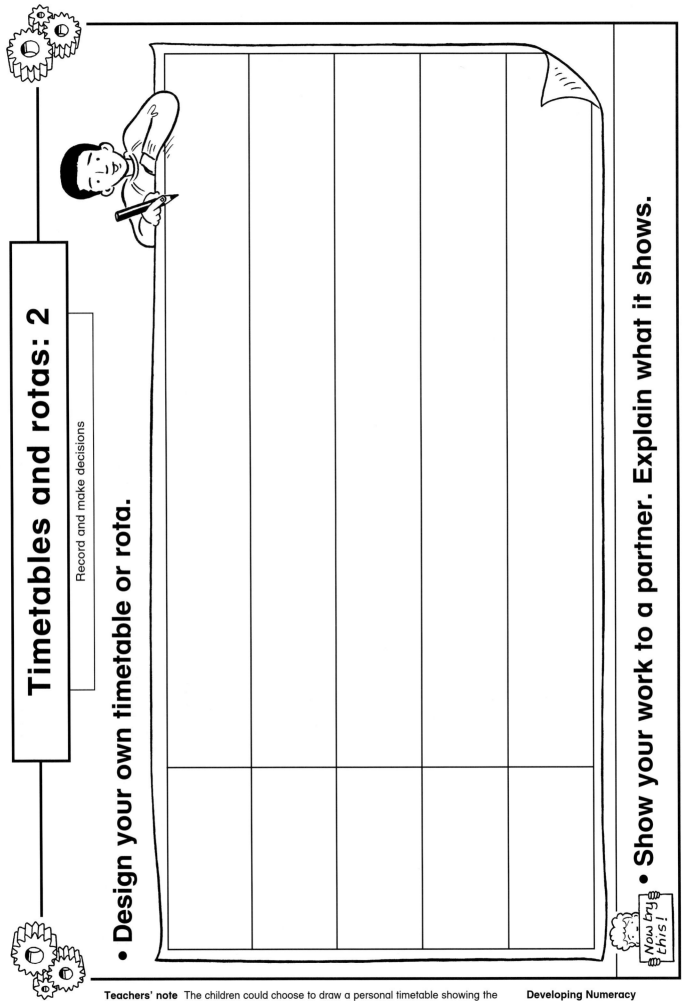

- Design your own timetable or rota.

- Show your work to a partner. Explain what it shows.

Now try this!

Teachers' note The children could choose to draw a personal timetable showing the order of the things they do in an average day (exact times are not important), or they could devise a group rota to allocate days or times of responsibility for classroom jobs. The children should be allowed to spend time making their own decisions and recording information as they choose (see page 11).

**Developing Numeracy
Using & Applying Maths
Year 2
© A & C BLACK**

Wriggling worms

- **<u>Without</u> measuring, list the worms in order of length. Start with the shortest. _____**

- **Now estimate the length of each worm.**

A	B	C	D	E	F
cm	cm	cm	cm	cm	cm

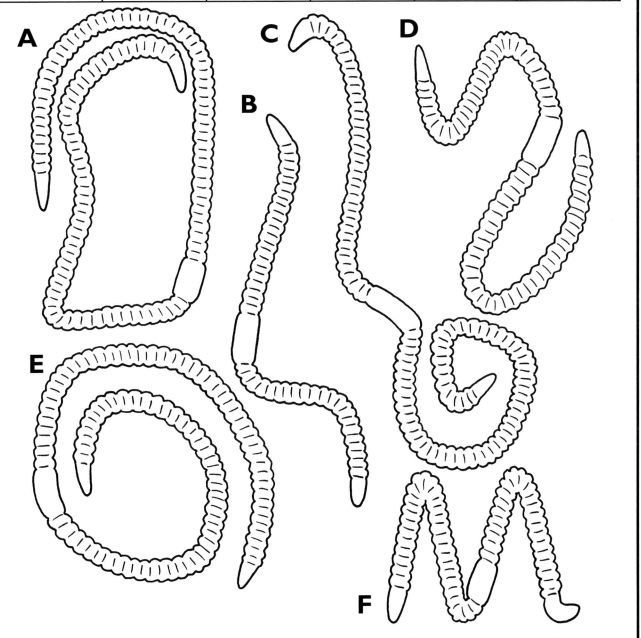

- **Check your estimates using string and a ruler.**

Teachers' note Provide string and rulers and ensure that the children know how to use them to measure the worms. Ask them to compare their estimates with their measurements. Stress that having the exact answer is not important, and that the more the children practise estimating, the better they will become. As an extension, ask the children to draw a wiggly worm (or make one out of Plasticine) that is about 30 cm in length, without measuring, then to check the length by measuring.

**Developing Numeracy
Using & Applying Maths
Year 2
© A & C BLACK**

41

Mystery tour

Make decisions and visualise

Ruby has planned a tour around the classroom.

She uses left **and** right .

She uses paces **to show distance.**

1. Start with your back to the board.
2. Turn left. Walk 5 paces.
3. Turn right. Walk 8 paces.
4. Turn right. Walk 2 paces.
5. Turn left. Walk 3 paces.
6. What can you see?

• **Make up a tour around your classroom or school.**

Use **left** and **right**.

Say how many **paces** to walk.

1. Start with your back to

    _____.
2. Turn _____. Walk _____ paces.
3. Turn _____. Walk _____ paces.
4. Turn _____. Walk _____ paces.
5. Turn _____. Walk _____ paces.
6. What can you see?

• **Swap with a partner and follow their tour.**

Some people's paces are different lengths.

Now try this!

• **Write a new tour using** metres **instead of paces.**

You need a metre stick or a trundle wheel.

Teachers' note The children could work in pairs or small groups to devise a tour. Explain that all the turns made in this activity are quarter turns. Begin the lesson by revising quarter turns and in particular left and right turns. This can be done as a whole class game in which the children stand on the spot and you call out instructions: for example, 'Turn left, turn left, turn right, turn left, turn right. What can you see?' Provide metre sticks or trundle wheels for the extension activity.

Developing Numeracy
Using & Applying Maths
Year 2
© A & C BLACK

Spinning around

Reason and look for patterns

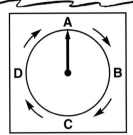

☆ **Always** start with the arrow at **A**. Move **clockwise**.

Cut out the pieces below to help you.

☆ If the arrow moves **1 quarter turn**, it points to **B**.

☆ If the arrow moves **2 quarter turns**, it points to **C**.

• **Write the letter the arrow points to after:**

4 quarter turns ☐   5 quarter turns ☐

8 quarter turns ☐   3 quarter turns ☐

6 quarter turns ☐   9 quarter turns ☐

7 quarter turns ☐   10 quarter turns ☐

• **How many quarter turns end on:**

A? __ __   B? _1_ __ __

C? _2_ __ __   D? __ __

Talk to a partner about what you notice.

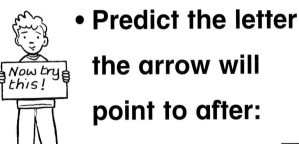

• **Predict the letter the arrow will point to after:**

12 quarter turns ☐

14 quarter turns ☐

• **Now check.**

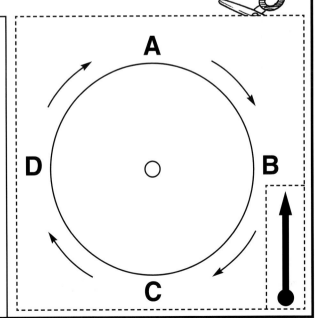

Teachers' note The children should cut out the dial and arrow at the bottom of the page so that they can find answers practically, and test their predictions in the extension activity. Remind them that the arrow should always point to A at the start. Encourage them to talk about any patterns they notice and to explain their thinking. Some children may benefit from using an enlarged copy of the dial and arrow. A split pin can then be used to fix the arrow to the centre of the dial.

**Developing Numeracy
Using & Applying Maths
Year 2
© A & C BLACK**

Balancing act

Use trial and improvement, and test your ideas

• **Work with a partner.**

You need interlocking cubes.

☆ Look at this model and read the colours. Now make the model. Stand it up so that only the **green cube** touches the table.

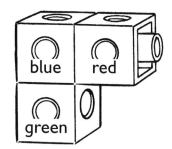
blue red
green

yellow

☆ Add a yellow cube to your model. Only the **green cube** can touch the table and the model must not fall over!

☆ Find all the places you <u>can</u> put the yellow cube. Find all the places you <u>cannot</u> put it. Talk to your partner.

• **How many places can you put the yellow cube in total?** ☐

• **Describe the places.** _____

_____

Now try this!

• **Now make this model.**

• **How many places can you put the yellow cube?** ☐

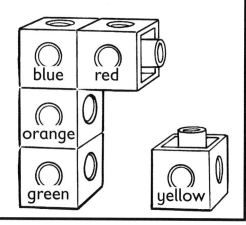
blue red
orange
green yellow

Teachers' note Red, blue, green, yellow and orange interlocking cubes are required for this activity. The sheet can be used in a variety of ways: a group of more confident children could be given the sheet and asked to work in small groups or pairs to tackle the investigation, or the activity could be talked through and carried out with the whole class so that findings are shared and discussed. See page 12 for ways of extending the investigation.

Developing Numeracy Using & Applying Maths Year 2 © A & C BLACK

Spot the shape

• **Play this game with a partner.**

You need two copies of this sheet.

☆ Cut out the cards from one sheet.
   Put them in a pile, face down.
   Keep the other sheet whole.

☆ Pick a card. Do <u>not</u> show it to your partner.

☆ Describe the shape. Can your partner point to the exact shape on the sheet?

☆ Swap roles and keep playing.

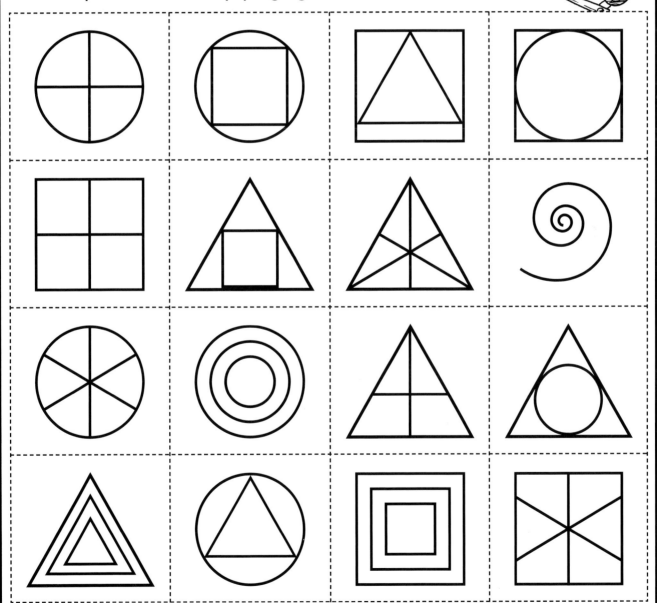

Teachers' note Each child will need one copy of this sheet. Ideally, the sheet to be cut up should be copied onto card so that the shapes cannot be seen through the paper. The other sheet should be kept whole. As an extension, ask the children to talk to each other about the shapes and to decide how they would like to sort them into sets. They could then stick the cards onto separate pieces of paper in their sets and record their reasons for sorting in this way.

Developing Numeracy
Using & Applying Maths
Year 2
© A & C BLACK

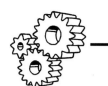

Jigsaw: 1

You need the jigsaw pieces from *Jigsaw: 2*.

• Write the letters of the:

four corner pieces | L | | | |

six pieces with one straight edge | | | | | | |

two pieces with **no** straight edges | | |

two pieces that are the same shape | | |

• Fit all the pieces together to make a rectangle. Write the letters below. Try different ways.

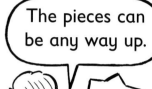
The pieces can be any way up.

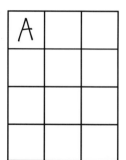

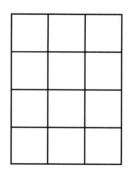

• Make these squares. Fill in the missing letters.

A	

A	J
L	C

C	A
J	L

• Take away C, L, E and H. Join the rest together in one straight line.

| | | | | | | | |

Teachers' note The children will need copies of page 47. Encourage them to ask their own questions and to arrange the pieces in different ways. Discuss that when making rectangles or squares, the edges must be straight lines and so the children should look carefully at which are corner pieces, side pieces or middle pieces. Ensure they realise that the pieces can be rotated: for example, 'J' in the diagram above may be the J piece on its side or upside down.

Developing Numeracy
Using & Applying Maths
Year 2
© A & C BLACK

Jigsaw: 2

Reason and use trial and improvement

• **Cut out each piece of the jigsaw.**

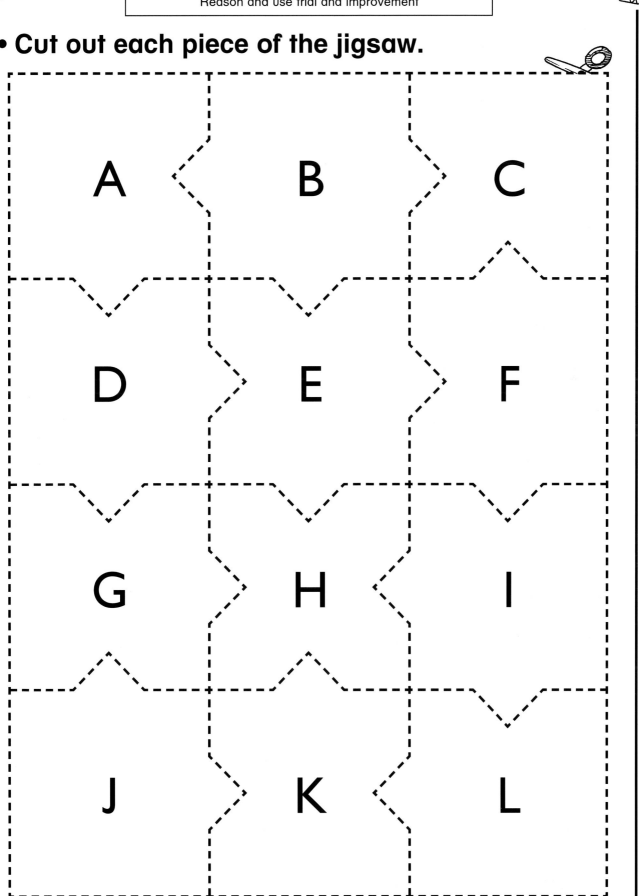

Teachers' note These jigsaw pieces should be cut out and used with the activity on page 46. If possible, copy the sheet onto thin card. The jigsaw pieces could be enlarged and laminated to create a more permanent resource. As an extension, the children could investigate other ways of joining the pieces together.

Developing Numeracy
Using & Applying Maths
Year 2
© A & C BLACK

Shape sequences

☆ Cut out the shape cards.

☆ Arrange the cards in a sequence. Number
them in the order you have chosen.

☆ Now compare your cards with your partner's.
Did you arrange them in the same way?

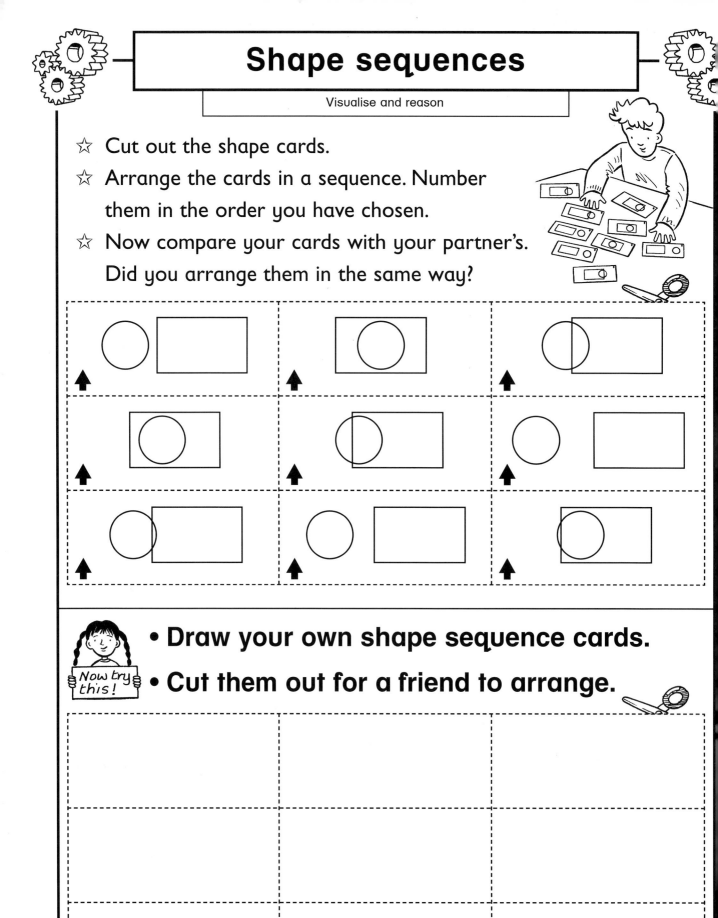

• **Draw your own shape sequence cards.**

• **Cut them out for a friend to arrange.**

Teachers' note Encourage the children to describe in their own words how they think the cards can be ordered. They should compare and discuss differences between their answers and those of a partner. The children could be asked to write a description of what happens to the shapes in the sequences. The cards can be coloured and displayed on the wall in or out of sequence, to stimulate further discussion.

**Developing Numeracy
Using & Applying Maths
Year 2
© A & C BLACK**